Usborne

The UNWORRY Drawing Book

Eddie Reynolds

Illustrated by
Harry Briggs

Designed by
Freya Harrison

With expert advice from Dr. Angharad Rudkin,
Clinical Child Psychologist, University of Southampton

DRAW YOUR WORRIES AWAY

Worries are a normal part of life. Some people worry a lot, others not so much. But even when worries feel big, there's ALWAYS a way to shrink them down. This drawing book is here to help you do just that.

Ahhh, now I feel MUCH better.

Drawing can really help you relax. Scientists think it can even help change the chemicals in your brain to create calm, worry-free thoughts.

HOW TO USE THIS BOOK

This book is packed with DRAWING activities to help you UNWORRY. Here are some examples.

Imagine a calm, faraway, magical world.

Try slow, soothing shading.

What happens when you draw with both hands at once?

Each activity comes with instructions or tips.
But really you can think of them as suggestions.
Follow them, or try something different.

If you ever worry
that your drawings aren't
quite right, remind yourself:

There is no
wrong way
to draw

A wise sloth once told me, it's not the final drawing that matters, but enjoying the time you spend making it. There's no rush, no target – just you and your drawings. Take as much time as you like.

All you need is a
pen or pencil (or a few).
You could even treat yourself
to some nice, fresh, NEW ones.

FIRST THINGS FIRST

Every time you sit down to draw, start by STRETCHING your arms, hands and fingers. When you worry, your body tenses up. Stretching RELAXES your muscles and releases soothing chemicals to your brain. This not only makes drawing easier - it makes you feel good, too.

1

Lay your hands on your lap, palms facing up.

Clench both hands tight to make a fist. Count to five, then relax. Try this a few times.

2

Hold out one arm flat in front of you, with your palm facing up.

Gently pull down your hand, like this, so that you feel a light stretch in your arm and wrist. Count to five, then let go.

Do the same on your other arm.

3

Relax your arms, hands and fingers, then stretch your fingers out wide, like this.

Count to three, then relax them.

1, 2, 3.

Do this five times.

4

Relax your wrists, then SHAKE your hands. Do this for as long as you like.

Now your hands are loose and limber, it's time to start drawing.
Try making a picture without taking your pencil off the page.
Let your hand glide, swoosh and squiggle.

You could draw...

...a surfer
riding a
wave

...a puppy

...a windmill

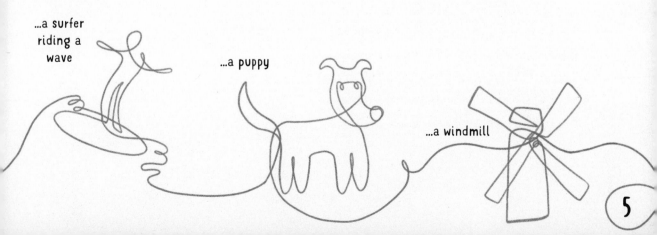

MINDFUL DRAWING

When your head is buzzing with thoughts,
you often stop noticing what's around you. A set of
techniques known as MINDFUL DRAWING can help you to focus
on the here and now. Slowly but surely, whooshing worries
will fizzle out of your head and your body will relax.

TRY THIS...

1

Pick something
around you to draw.

A photograph

A vase of
flowers

Your
reflection

2

Draw it, but don't look at the paper.
Instead, keep looking at the object
you're drawing. As you do so, notice
how your focus slides away from your
thoughts onto the movements of the
hand you draw with.

3

When you think it's
ready, take a look.

Your drawing probably won't turn out as you imagined. But your brain will have sent relaxing messages to your body while you did it.

Heehee. That doesn't look like me!

FEEL, LOOK, LISTEN

Sketching can always be mindful, no matter WHAT you draw. If you pay attention to what you FEEL, SEE, SMELL and HEAR, your body and mind will settle.

Start simple. Cover this page with drawings of LEAVES. They don't have to look real - you could fill them with dots, squirls and patterns. Focus on what drawing FEELS like, more than how it looks.

To draw a leaf, draw the outline first...

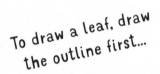

...then fill it in.

Listen to the sound of your pencil or pen swooshing across the page.

Notice the smell of this book – and the room you're in.

Run your fingers across the paper.

How does it feel?

Breathe in... breathe out. Pay attention to your breathing. Does it slow down? Get deeper? Or change another way?

9

WAY UP HIGH

Fill this page with BIRDS of all sorts. Perch them on a branch, or draw them soaring off into the sky. Imagine them taking your worries with them as they fly away.

A bird begins life as an egg – when you draw one, as well as in real life. Scribble an egg-shaped blob for the body...

...then add legs, wings, tail feathers and a head.

If you place the different parts like this, it looks as if the bird is flying.

Wow, look at that one!

A bird
can have...

...a big
beak.

...a fancy,
feathery
tail.

...a tuft on
its head.

...a long neck
and legs.

START WITH A SCRIBBLE

Sometimes, it can be hard to decide what to draw - especially if your head is heavy with worries. Whenever that happens, try just SCRIBBLING, then turn the doodles into something else. It might UNBLOCK your thoughts.

An eye-catching hairstyle

You could try to spot an outline of something in your scribbles.

Land ahoy!

Or if you can't see anything in particular, just fill the shapes with patterns.

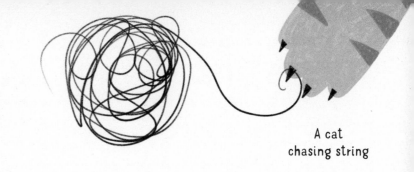

A cat
chasing string

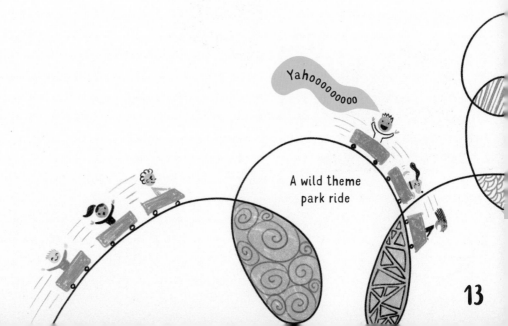

Yahoooooooooo

A wild theme
park ride

13

SHADING

SHADING is a particularly soothing technique that adds SHADOW to your drawing.

Simply rub your pencil up and down gently on its side, and repeat the same, soft scribbling action.

Sketch shadows onto these pictures. Remember shadows can be long or short.

The shape doesn't have to be exact. Focus on the FEEL of the pencil against your fingers as you swoosh it back and forth.

Shading can make a flat shape look like a real object.

You can make a flat CIRCLE...

   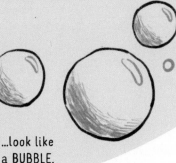

...look like a BUBBLE.

Shade in this giant balloon.

Press down firmly to get a dark shade, and gently to get a light shade.

This side will be darker, because the Sun is on the other side.

Shadows can also show how far away something is from the ground.

If you draw a thin shadow from the sloth's toes, it'll look as if it's standing on the floor.

If you scribble a shadow lower down, it will look as if it's floating up, up and away...

TWO HANDS

When you draw with BOTH hands at once, the feeling is so NEW and unusual that moving your hands takes up ALL your attention. There's not much room left for worries. It's easier than it sounds – your stronger hand GUIDES the weaker one.

Here's how you do it:

1 Start the drawing at the top, with both pencils.

2 Make your way down to the bottom, drawing both sides at once.

3 Fill in the outline with both hands.

Fill the space with two-handed drawings.

It's easiest if you draw something where both halves are roughly the same – like ME. There are more ideas below.

Buildings

Bugs and butterflies

Trees and flowers

Patterns

Faces

A circus tent

17

CALM CLOTHES

Fashion designers sketch their ideas before they create new clothes. They often start by making a MOOD BOARD. That means choosing a THEME, then jotting down words and pictures that fit it.

Create a mood board for the theme...

CALMNESS

What words, colours, places and things does the word CALM make you think of?

Blossom

Fluffy clouds

Ripples

Sometimes, simply thinking of things that make you feel calm can be enough to relax your head and DISTRACT you from worries.

Here's a space to design clothes inspired by your mood board. You could sketch a hat, shorts, a t-shirt...

...or clothes that are EXTRA good for relaxing, like mine.

Blossom onesie

Fluffy cloud slippers

CARTOON FACES

When drawing CARTOON FACES, dots, squiggles and simple shapes are enough to make all kinds of expressions.
Try it out for yourself below.

You can draw a MOUTH as a single line, open wide, or you can draw lips.

Ears sit roughly halfway up the face, in line with the eyes.

Eyes are normally higher up than noses, which are higher up than mouths. In cartoons, you can move them around.

If you find making mistakes stressful, inventing cartoon faces makes a nice, stress-free activity. It encourages you to try unusual designs without the fear of going wrong – because you can't.

WORRY CHARACTER

It can be helpful to picture your worries as an IMAGINARY CHARACTER. Whenever you worry, think of your character. Then, imagine something happening to it that makes it - and your worries - disappear.

Design your character here.

It could be...

...something that reflects how you feel?

...a harmless, silly creature that's too cute to find scary?

Naming your character can be helpful. It gives you a word to use when you talk and think about your worries.

NAME IT:

. . . .

. . . .

. . . .

Draw something happening to your character - SHRINK it, TRAP it, or STOP it in its tracks. YOU'RE in control of your feelings - not the other way around.

This wall is too tall for you!

You could also sketch your character then SCRIBBLE IT OUT. Or draw it, shut the book, and leave your worries here.

LESS CAN BE MORE

If you draw a picture using only two or three colours, it's called LIMITING YOUR PALETTE. It's relaxing, because you don't have to keep choosing new colours.

DRAWING GAMES

Two quick fixes for a worry-filled head are LAUGHING and SMILING. They release feel-good chemicals called endorphins into your brain. Here's a game you can play with yourself. See if it brings a grin to your face.

You can use a dice, or play without.

1 Roll a DICE until you get two different numbers in a row. OR, close your eyes and prod one FINGER in the blue box at least twice, until you land on two different numbers. The numbers tell you which animals to combine to make a new, made-up creature.

Walrus

Butterfly

Kangaroo

Flamingo

Octopus

Bushbaby

2 Draw your mish-mashed creatures and name them.

A pink-winged butterbaby

I'm THREE
animals in one.

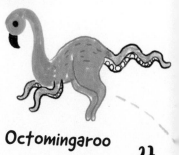

Octomingaroo

HERE'S ANOTHER DRAWING GAME

1

Close your eyes, then prod your finger somewhere in this box of animal names.

2

Draw the animal you land on, but with a HORN, like a unicorn. You could name it, too.

Hamsticorn

There's space to add more animal names if you like.

Bumblebee   **Duck**

Hamster   **Tiger**

Giraffe   Ant

Otter   **Toad**

Rhino   CAT

POLAR BEAR

Did you know that you can actually TRICK your brain into feeling good? If you put a pen between your teeth and don't bite into it, your brain releases endorphins because it thinks you're SMILING.

Ooh, my horn's a traffic cone.

Mine lights up!

Uni-tiger

Elephanticorn

TAKE A CLOSER LOOK

Find something around you that you can LOOK AT and TOUCH as you draw it. A piece of fruit or a mug would work. Examine it REEEALLY closely before you make a start on your picture.

HOLD IT

How does it feel? Is it the same texture all over, or does it change?

LOOK AND LOOK AGAIN

The closer you look at something, the more details you notice. What can you spot?

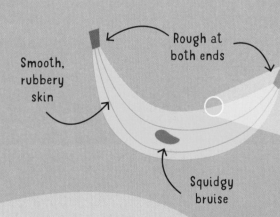

Smooth, rubbery skin

Rough at both ends

Squidgy bruise

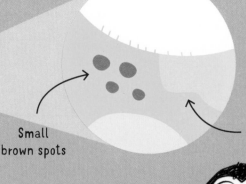

Small brown spots

Three different yellows

Touching the object that you're drawing is a MINDFULNESS technique.

Using your hands is proven to give your mind the quiet it needs to focus and be calm.

Here's a space to draw your picture.
Try to include all the details you noticed,
and any new ones you spot as you go.

MOVERS AND SHAKERS

Keep your brain distracted by picturing yourself
in this bustling park. Fill it with people running,
jumping, dancing... show them MOVING.

Here's a quick
way to draw
moving people.

1

You can start with a
simple stick figure,
drawn in faint pencil.

2

Draw an
outline on top.

3

Fill it in and
add details.

Lines like this
show SPEED.

Arrange the arms, legs, body and
head in different positions, to show
a range of movements.

FAR, FAR AWAY...

...in a magical land that has not yet been drawn, there live a queen and king who love to relax.

Can you design their kingdom? It should be peaceful, calm and welcoming – a world that you can visit in your head whenever your thoughts feel too heavy or busy.

When you imagine somewhere peaceful,
your brain thinks that you're actually there.
It sends signals to your body telling it to relax.
This trick is known as ESCAPISM.

ASK YOURSELF...

Where do the queen and king live?

What colour will everything be?

What sounds and smells might there be?

Will there be plants and animals? Real or made-up?

Will the ground be hilly or flat? Watery or dry? Soft or hard?

CUTE ART

There's a simple type of modern Japanese drawing that tries to make everything look ADORABLE – be it a cactus, a mug or a cat. It's called Kawaii (say "Ka-why-ee") and it means "cute" in Japanese.

This cat drawing is Kawaii.

It has a thick, simple outline.

There are BLOCKS of colour – no gradual shading.

Almost all the lines are CURVED – even some of the corners.

It has a FACE, with eyes wide apart, pink circles for cheeks, and a mouth not far below the eyes.

Pick a few things from around you to draw in Kawaii style on these shelves.

Here's a TIP. Experiment with simple outlines in pencil. Once you're happy, draw over it in felt tip, then fill it in.

Don't worry if your drawing doesn't look much like the real thing. We look cute BECAUSE our outlines are very simple, not realistic.

Some Kawaii face ideas:

If you're stuck, you could copy the drawings already here.

NO RULES

Sometimes, working without rules and instructions can be very freeing. In the early 20th century, a group of artists known as SURREALISTS really disliked rules, so they created art where rules are BANNED.

THAT MEANS...

...they drew whatever popped into their heads, with no plan, to see what came out. They called this AUTOMATIC DRAWING.

DRAW LIKE A SURREALIST

And remember – it doesn't have to make ANY sense, AT ALL.

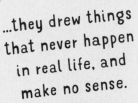
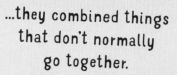

...they drew things that never happen in real life, and make no sense.

...they combined things that don't normally go together.

Ugh – it's raining moustaches. Now my legs are melting.

OCEAN DEEP

Immerse yourself in a magnificent underwater world.
Fill it with fish, coral, seahorses and more, as your pencil
swims across the page. Take a deep, calming breath... and dive in.

To draw a FISH, choose a
shape for its body...

...then add fins, a tail, eyes,
mouth and scales...

...and maybe
bubbles, too.

To draw CORAL, sketch a rock, then
add coral poking out from behind.

To listen to calm ocean sounds while you draw, go to usborne.com/Quicklinks and search UNWORRY DRAWING. There, you'll find links to websites with relaxing sounds, and other unworry activities.

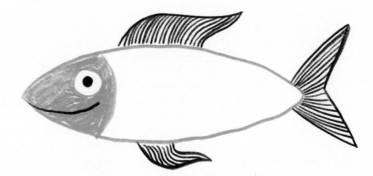

Coral can be...

...tall and spindly.

...round and bobbly.

...a mix of colours.

TO THE RESCUE!

Sometimes worries give you unkind thoughts about yourself - maybe that you're not good enough, brave enough, or something similar. One solution is a CONFIDENCE BOOST. Try this - picture yourself as a mighty SUPERHERO with the power to DEFEAT ALL WORRIES.

TO DRAW YOURSELF AS A SUPERHERO...

Choose a shape for the body...

...add a triangle...

...then arms and legs.

Draw your face and hair in cartoon style (see page 20).

Add a cape...

...and a logo.

If you want to show yourself FLYING, draw the parts sideways on.

WHOOOOSH

Comic book artists who draw superheroes often write SOUND EFFECTS, too.

Here's some space to design a poster of your superhero. While you draw, remind yourself how BRAVE and GREAT you are.

You can choose ANY superpower.

Shapeshifting?

SUPER SPEED?

Laser beams?

Healing power?

SUPER STRENGTH?

Is there anything you wish you could CONTROL? That could be your power.

Time?

The weather?

Move things with your mind?

DRAW EVERY DAY

Starting a ROUTINE where you take time every day to relax with something you enjoy doing can stop little worries from growing too big.

Try to spend a quiet moment each day for a week DRAWING. Even if it's just for five minutes, it can give your head time to be peaceful.

These words might spark ideas...

summer

adventure

patterns

feast

outer space

forest

snowflake

magic

DAY 1

How do you feel after, compared to before you started? Circle your answer each day.

 Better

 No different

DAY 2

I feel...

 Better

 No different

DAY 3

I feel...

 Better

 No different

DAY 4

I feel...

 Better

 No different

DAY 5

I feel...

 Better

 No different

mountains   **funny faces**   DRAGON   *fireworks*

46   TREEHOUSE   FLYING   **dream**   *waterslide*

DAY 6

I feel...

 Better

 No different

DAY 7

I feel...

 Better

 No different

gymnastics   *DANCING*   the ancient past

ocean waves   celebration   **DINOSAURS**

LOTS OF DOTS

Try making a picture using only DOTS. It's a slow, gentle, REPETITIVE technique, known as POINTILLISM. Small, repeated actions can help settle anxious thoughts, by fixing your focus on something simple.

Continue this enchanted forest or start something completely different.

TIPS

Draw the outline first, then fill it with more dots.

Dots close together look DARKER...

...and dots far apart look LIGHTER.

Try dotting different colours near each other. This is called BLENDING.

Dot drawings can take a loooong time – and that's fine! Go slow. You can come back to it again and again.

ONE SHAPE

Try drawing using ONLY triangles, or circles, or rectangles. Setting yourself LIMITS forces you to "think outside the box". Thinking in a NEW way can help UNTANGLE knotty thoughts that go round in circles in your head.

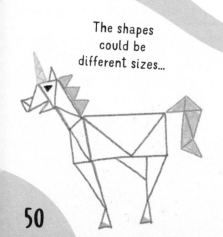

The shapes could be different sizes...

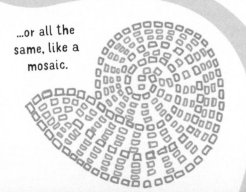

...or all the same, like a mosaic.

FRUIT & VEG ART

Here's another idea. Make a picture out of drawings of fruit and vegetables - perhaps a landscape, a musical instrument or a face.

It can help if you sketch a faint outline first, then think of fruit and veg that are a similar shape to each part.

You can fill in any gaps with smaller fruits, such as grapes or berries.

RAINDROPS

There's a calming magic to watching raindrops trickle down glass. Imagine these pages are a window and rain is pitter-pattering against it. Fill it with watery trickles and droplets.

1

To draw a water droplet, you start with the outline.

2

Next, gently SHADE the inside. See page 14 to remind yourself how.

The sides are lighter than the middle, with a large light patch down one side.

Some raindrops sit still. Here, leave a light patch near the top.

Others flow down and leave a faint trail behind them.

To feel cosy listening to rain as you draw, go to Usborne Quicklinks and search UNWORRY DRAWING. There, you'll find links to videos with calming rain sounds.

WORD ART

Reading and listening to calm, comforting WORDS can settle whizzing thoughts and give your brain some peace and quiet. Try building a picture out of soothing words by making shapes as you write.

1

Decide what you want to draw, then draw a faint outline in pencil.

2

Fill in the outline with words related to the drawing - perhaps a sentence, or a collection of calming words.

sky soft white moonlight still glow night calm silent night sky word awe crescent still big

3

You could rub out the outline once you've finished.

sky soft white moonlight still glow night calm silent night sky word crescent awe still big

HOOT HER gentle wing glides through the night eyes glow gold with FEATHERS light HOOT

It's easiest to fit words inside SIMPLE shapes. For more detailed drawings, you could add details around the words.

The letters can vary in size.

The words can go in any direction.

TIPS

You could find a poem, song or story and draw what it describes. Maybe even write your own.

Poems about nature or nighttime are often gentle and peaceful.

If you're stuck, here are some words to use.

warm   peaceful   **soft**

HUG   bliss

smooth   quiet

PILLOW   lullaby

You could look up these words in a thesaurus or dictionary for even more inspiration.

hush   **sleepy**

DECORATE ME

Here's a gentle distraction from whatever's on your mind. DECORATE the vase and then the rug with PATTERNS. Draw slowly, deliberately, and concentrate on the shapes you make.

Drawing with a limited palette might feel EXTRA soothing (see page 24).

A pattern of repeated images or symbols is known as a MOTIF.

Combining shapes creates a design called a GEOMETRIC pattern.

ZOOM OUT

Making yourself feel TINY can make your problems feel tiny too. If you realize how small you are compared to the big, wide world and everything that's happening right NOW, your thoughts feel less important. That makes them much easier to deal with. It's a very FREEING feeling.

TRY THIS...

1

Draw yourself, very small, in this circle.

2

Now draw some of the things around you.

3

Sketch a few buildings, real or made-up.

4

Fill this space with pictures of things from even FURTHER away, such as rainforests, deserts, people, plants and animals. Imagine being there with them.

5

What's even bigger than the world? The UNIVERSE. Draw planets, stars, and faraway galaxies.

ZOOMING OUT like this is known as DECENTRING yourself. If you pay too much attention to your thoughts, you feel as if life happens AROUND you. When you become AWARE of other things, your thoughts feel like a small part of a much **BIGGER** picture.

SNOOOOOOOZERS

Learn how to draw some
of the world's sleepiest, snooziest
creatures. This is a great activity for a tired
brain – the step-by-step instructions mean you don't have to think very much.

ARMADILLO

1

Draw a circle with
a slice cut out, like this.

2

Add a long, thin head...

...with an ear at the top and
lines for an eye and the mouth.

3

Draw an arm and a
leg in the middle...

...and a small tail
at the bottom.

Armadillos like me sleep for
16 hours each day, curled up
on our sides. We mostly doze
off undergound.

4

Add a pattern to the shell
and colour in your drawing.

Draw your
armadillo
here.

KOALA

1

Draw two round blobs, like this.

2

Add big round ears, eyebrows...

...lines for eyes, a big nose and a mouth.

3

Draw a big "C" from the middle of the body to below the bottom.

4

Draw ONE of its feet and one of its arms, like this.

I snooze for 18 to 22 hours each day, tucked in a nook up a tree or hugging a branch.

5

Draw a branch or a tree trunk....

...then fill in your drawing and add short lines for fur.

Draw your koala here.

THANK YOU!

Psychologists say that thinking of things you're GRATEFUL for can make you feel HAPPIER and more HOPEFUL. Drawing those things brings them to the FRONT of your mind, and lifts up your mood.

Make a list of things that you're thankful for.

Things that make you laugh?

Silly faces!

People you love to spend time with?

Something useful?

Something fun?

Your favourite...

...food?

...place?

...birthday gift?

Draw a few things from your list in the frames below to create
your own personal ART GALLERY. You can look at it when you feel
worried to remind yourself of what you LOVE about your life.

IF YOU'RE STILL WORRIED...

Often, worries drift into your head
for a short while, then drift out and are
gone for good. Activities such as drawing, doodling,
making things and moving around are excellent ways to
nudge worries in the right direction.

But sometimes, worries might keep coming back. If unwelcome thoughts
start to take over, it's important to TALK to a grown-up you trust, perhaps
a parent or a teacher, and tell them how you feel. They will be able to
listen and help you find a way to turn worries down.

Additional illustration by
Freya Harrison

Design manager:
Stephen Moncrieff

Edited by
Jane Chisholm

First published in 2021 by Usborne Publishing Ltd., Usborne House, 83-85 Saffron Hill,
London EC1N 8RT, England, usborne.com Copyright © 2021 Usborne Publishing Ltd.